A Visit to San Francisco

by Cynthia Benjamin

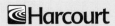

Harcourt

Orlando   Boston   Dallas   Chicago   San Diego

Visit *The Learning Site!*

www.harcourtschool.com

Dear Grandma,

We arrived in San Francisco last night. Our hotel is near San Francisco Bay. Dad said there is water on three sides of the city. Because it's summer, it's foggy. Sometimes I hear a strange, loud noise. What could it be?

San Francisco

San Francisco is built on more than forty hills. When I look out my window, I can see some of them far away. This is definitely an amazing city.

Love,
Cindy

Dragon Gate entrance to Chinatown

Dear Grandma,

There are many different neighborhoods in San Francisco. This morning we went to one of them. It's called Chinatown. We walked through Dragon Gate to begin our visit.

4

Chinatown is full of restaurants and shops. Some stores sell special Chinese foods, such as dried fish. Others sell carved jade jewelry. An assistant in one store showed me some wind chimes. They made a beautiful sound in the breeze.

Love,
Cindy

A street in Chinatown

Dear Grandma,

Today Mom, Dad, and I went walking in the city. We went to a neighborhood called Telegraph Hill. Many years ago people sent signals from there to sailing ships. In those days Telegraph Hill was covered with grass, and sheep grazed there.

Telegraph Hill rises high above the rest of the city.

A street of stairs in Telegraph Hill

Today Telegraph Hill looks very different. There is a steep cliff on the east side of the hill. Mom, Dad, and I climbed all 377 steps to the very top! When we returned to the hotel, we were really tired.

Love,
Cindy

Dear Grandma,

After yesterday's climb, we were glad to ride a cable car. I was positive that cable cars had engines, but I was wrong. A steel cable under the street pulls the heavy cars along.

A San Francisco cable car

Riding the cable car was fun! One person drives it. Another worker uses a lever that grabs the cable and moves the car. Cable cars make a loud clanking noise. Is that what I heard the other day?

Love,
Cindy

Golden Gate Bridge

Dear Grandma,

We visited Aunt Ellen today. Dad drove across the Golden Gate Bridge to get to her house. It's one of the longest bridges in the world—almost 9,000 feet! I'll be more specific. The bridge is exactly 8,981 feet long.

You can walk or ride your bike across the bridge, too. If you do, it's fun to look up at the tall red towers on either end. When we drove across, we saw big ships on their way to the Pacific Ocean.

Love,
Cindy

The hippos at the San Francisco Zoo

Dear Grandma,

We spent the whole day at the San Francisco Zoo. It's a special zoo because it has very few cages. Most of the animals live in areas without bars. Zoo workers and animal doctors take good care of them.

In the morning we saw polar bears, kangaroos, and monkeys. Then we visited the lion house. Dad wanted to see Prince Charles, a very rare white tiger. Later we went to the children's zoo. I saw sheep, goats, and ponies in the barnyard.

Love,
Cindy

Prince Charles, a very rare white tiger

Fishing boats at Fisherman's Wharf

Dear Grandma,

Mom couldn't wait to see Fisherman's Wharf. Many people who fish keep their boats there. We went early in the morning, when it was still foggy. While Mom and Dad talked to a fisher, I heard that same strange noise. It seemed closer now.

I wanted to have fresh fish for lunch. Some workers cooked shrimp and crab in large metal pots right on the sidewalk. After we ate, we looked in the shops along Fisherman's Wharf.

Love,
Cindy

Cooking fresh seafood at Fisherman's Wharf

Fisherman's Wharf at night

Dear Grandma,

   The last night of our trip, we returned to Fisherman's Wharf. After dinner, we looked at San Francisco Bay. Then I heard that strange sound again. I felt like a detective who had solved a big case. It was a foghorn!

Love,
Cindy